Chicken by Che

Tana Reiff

A Pacemaker **LifeTimes™ 2** Book

Simon & S

LifeTimes™ 2 Titles

Take Away Three
Climbing the Wall
The Door Is Open
Just for Today
Chicken by Che
Play Money
The Missing Piece

Cover illustration: Arthur Koch

Library of Congress
Catalog Card Number: 87-80038

ISBN 0-8224-4606-5
Printed in the United States of America

10 9 8 7 6 5

Contents

CHAPTER 1

The chicken
tasted just right.
The vegetables
were fresh and hot.
Che Acosta cooked
the best French food
in town.
There was
a crowd
every night
at the French restaurant.

But Che
was not as happy
as the crowd.
He wanted
his own restaurant.
He wanted
to cook
for his own neighbors.

He wanted
to cook chicken
his own way.

Che looked up.
Two people walked
into the kitchen.

"We are
Mr. and Mrs. Glass,"
said Mr. Glass.
He shook
Che's hand.
"Our meal
was very, very fine.
This is
the best French food
outside of France!"

"Thank you,"
said Che.
"I am happy
to hear that."

"Maybe you
should have

your own restaurant."
said Mr. Glass.

Che thought
Mr. Glass
could read
his mind.

"I think about that
very often,"
said Che.

"I work
at the bank,"
said Mr. Glass.
"If you ever
start a restaurant
and you need
a loan,
let me know.
First put a plan together.
Then come see me.
Maybe I can help."

Che shook hands
again with Mr. and Mrs. Glass.

"I'll think
about the idea,"
said Che.
"Thank you very much."

   "Good night now,"
said Mr. Glass.
"And don't forget
what I said."

Thinking It Over

1.   Why would someone like Che
     want to start a restaurant?

2.   Do you believe
     it helps to know people
     "in the right places"?

3.   Why would Che need a loan
     to start a restaurant?

CHAPTER 2

Che knew
what he wanted
in a restaurant.
It would not be French.
The food
would not cost much.
The main dish
would be chicken.
Che would call
the restaurant
Chicken by Che.

Che knew
the right spot
for the restaurant.
There was
an empty lot.
It was
at the corner
of Second and Green streets.

Chicken by Che
would be open
from morning to midnight.
Che would need
four cooks.
He would need
four people
for the front counter.
Two cooks
and two counter persons
would work
at one time.

Chicken by Che
would have
the best chicken
in town.
People would come
from far and wide.
And then
they would come back
for more.

Che told
his wife, Norma,

and his three children
about his idea.
The kids
loved it.
"We could eat
chicken every day!"
they screamed.

But Norma
was not so sure.
"The restaurant business
is very hard,"
she said.
"You won't make money
for a long time.
You do this, Che,
if you want to.
But now we must
begin to save money."

"It will work,"
said Che.
"And we will
make money
sooner than you think."

Thinking It Over

1. Have you ever had an idea
    you were sure would work
    before you tried it?
    What made you so sure?

2. Why does it take a long time
    for a new business
    to make money?

3. What kind of business
    would you open?

CHAPTER 3

Che wrote
a business plan.
It had been
in his mind
for a long time.
Now he put it
down on paper.
He added up
how much money
he would need.

Then Che
took his business plan
to the bank.
He asked Mr. Glass
for a loan.
Mr. Glass said
the business plan
looked very clear.
He asked Che
some questions.

He wrote down
all the facts
he needed.

Mr. Glass called
a few days later.
"You got
a loan!"
he said.
"But you will need
more money than
you asked for.
The city
has a special program.
It is
for new businesses
in your neighborhood.
I think
you can get
the rest of the money
from the city program."

Che gave his business plan
to the city.
In a few months
the city gave him

the rest of the money.
It seemed
almost too easy.

Che left
his job.
The French restaurant
was very sorry
to see him go.

Che worked hard
on his chicken recipe.
He worked on it
every day.
He made it perfect.

Next, Che worked
with a builder.
Together they
planned the restaurant.
The builder planned
most of the outside.
Che planned
most of the inside.
Every part
of the building

had to meet
city building codes.

Then Che went
to a restaurant supply store.
He picked out
some tables and chairs.
They were
blue and red.
They would
look fine.

At last
the restaurant
was built.
Then it was time
to find workers.
Che put
a "Help Wanted" sign
in the window.
Almost 100 people
from the neighborhood
wanted a job.
Che could pick
only eight.

Thinking It Over

1. How would you pick
    people to work for you?

2. Why must buildings
    meet city codes?

3. Why are there special programs
    to help new businesses?

CHAPTER 4

It was
the "Grand Opening"
of Chicken by Che.
Many people
from the neighborhood
showed up.
They drank
free soft drinks.
They ate chicken
and more chicken.
They loved
Che's special recipe.
The grand opening
turned into a grand party.

"We love your chicken!"
they called to Che.
"We'll be back!"

Most of them
did come back

a few times.
For the first few weeks,
Chicken by Che
was very busy.
Che loved to see
every table full
of people.

But at times
there were not enough workers
to keep up.
People had to wait
for their food.
Some of them
got angry.
They didn't like
to wait
when they were hungry.

One day
the restaurant
was having
a big rush at lunch.
The line of people
ran all the way
out the front door.

All of a sudden,
the main stove
broke down.
Everything came
to a stop.

Che came
out front
to talk
to the people.
"I'm sorry,"
he said.
"Our kitchen is
out of order.
We can't cook
the chicken today."

Che lost
a lot of money
that day.
The stove
was fixed
by the next day.
But would
the angry people
come back?

Thinking It Over

1.   Would you go back
to a restaurant
that made you wait too long
for your food?

2.   When in your life
did something go wrong
at just the wrong time?

CHAPTER 5

People did
come back
to Chicken by Che.
Che felt
much better.
"I hope
nothing else
goes wrong,"
he said.

But a week later
something else did go wrong.
Near closing time
two men came
into the restaurant.
They wore masks
pulled down
over their faces.
"Put your hands up,"
they said.

"Now give us
all the money."

    The counter workers
gave the men
all the money.

    "Now turn around,"
said the two men.
"Everyone walk
into the back room."

    The workers
walked into the back room.
The two men
locked the door.
They took off
with the money.

    The police
drove by
the restaurant
at 1:00 in the morning.
They saw

that the lights
were still on.
They didn't see
any people.
They went inside
to see
what was wrong.

The police
found the workers
in the back room.
No one
was hurt.
But the robbers
were long gone
with the money.

Mr. Glass
from the bank
called Che
a few days later.
"Your money
is late this month,"
he said.

"I don't have it,"
said Che.
"We were robbed
a few nights ago.
I will have
the money
by next week."

"I hope so,"
said Mr. Glass.
"This is important."

Thinking It Over

1. What would you do
   if someone tried
   to rob you?

2. What happens
   if you pay the bank
   a little bit late?

3. What happens
   if you don't pay the bank at all?

CHAPTER 6

After the robbery,
business was slow.
People had heard
about the robbery.
They were afraid
to come to the restaurant.

Very little money
was coming in.
A week later
Che still didn't have
enough to pay the bank.

So Che
called a meeting
of all his workers.
"How can we
get more people
into the restaurant?"
he asked them.

A cook named Jose
had an idea.
"Every person
who comes in
could fill out
a paper,"
said Jose.
"Once a week
we can draw
a name.
The person we pick
will win
a free chicken dinner
for six people."

All the workers
liked the idea.
So did Che.

"I hope this works,"
he said to the workers.
"I don't want
to lay off any of you."

Then Che called
the police.

He wanted
to make sure
it was OK
to run the drawing.

The police wanted to know
all about the drawing.
They said
it would be OK
if Che followed
all the rules.

Thinking It Over

1. What does it mean
   to be laid off from a job?

2. Do you like drawings?
   Why?

3. Why did the police
   need to know
   about the drawing?

CHAPTER 7

The drawing
brought lots of people
to the restaurant.
The first winner
was a poor family.
Che was glad
they won.
This family
really needed
a free chicken dinner.

Che was also glad
for all the new business.
Now he had
enough money
to pay the bank.
Things were
looking up.

The next week a cook
left his job.

He didn't like
working at night.

Then one of the counter workers
left her job, too.
She was
going to have a baby.
She didn't feel
well enough
to work.

No one
wanted to work
during the holiday season.
Che was glad
he didn't
have to lay off anyone.
But he had to make do
with too few workers.

It made everyone
too busy.
Mistakes began
to happen.

A lady found
a bug in her chicken.
She called
the board of health.

The board of health
came to look over
the restaurant.
They told Che
to be more careful.
They made him
pay a fine.

Once again that month,
Che did not have
enough money
to pay the bank.

Then Che found
something worse.
One night
he was counting
his money.
Something was wrong.
He seemed to be

a hundred dollars short.
Something like this
had never
happened before.
He counted the money again.
There was no mistake
about it.
A hundred dollars
was missing!

Thinking It Over

1.   What could have happened
      to the hundred dollars?

2.   Would you want to work
      during the holiday season?

3.   Why does the board of health
      check on restaurants?

CHAPTER 8

Where was
the missing money?
Che had no idea.
Maybe
someone took it.
Che didn't say anything
to the workers.

During the next months,
workers came and went.
As one left,
a new one began.
Every new worker
had to be trained.
That took time.
And time was money.

One new worker
started a fire
in the stove.

The fire department
had to come
to put it out.

Insurance paid
to fix the stove.
But it took time
to fix it.
Che lost more money
while the stove
didn't work.

The fire
had messed up
the kitchen, too.
Jose said
he would clean it up.
"Don't give me
any money,"
he said.
"I want to help.
We must stick together."
Che said
that was very nice.

Jose did
a beautiful job.
The kitchen
looked like new.

Che was
very happy
with Jose.
He made Jose
his number-two person.
He gave him
a raise.
Che did not want Jose
to leave
like the others.

Thinking It Over

1. Why is a good worker
    so important to a business?

2. How does insurance work?

3. How can time be money?

CHAPTER 9

Che's wife, Norma,
cooked him
a special dinner
for his birthday.
So Che
left the restaurant
early that night
to have dinner
with his family.

After dinner
he came back
to the restaurant.
He wanted
to close things up.

When Che drove up,
he could see
that all the workers
had left.

Only Jose
was still there.
"Good kid,"
said Che to himself.

Che walked up
to the door.
Jose did not
see him coming.
Che saw something
he wished
he wasn't seeing.
Jose was taking money
from the cash register.

Che went inside.
"What are you doing?"
he asked Jose.

Jose did not know
what to say.

"Are you
stealing money?"
Che asked.

"Please, Che,"
begged Jose.
"I'm sorry.
I'll never do it again."

"Jose, Jose,"
cried Che.
"You were
my best worker.
You were
my number-two person.
Now I can
never be sure
of you again.
I must
fire you."

"I understand,"
said Jose.
"I'm sorry."

"Did you
ever steal
from me before?"
Che asked him.

Jose looked
at the floor.
"I won't lie to you,"
he said.
"I took
a hundred dollars."

"I want it back,"
said Che.
"You go now.
But someday
I want
that money back."

Jose put
his Chicken by Che cap
on the table.
Then he left.

Che felt
very sad
about Jose.
He had had high hopes
for Jose.
Now he was gone.

Thinking It Over

1.   How had Jose
     been trying to cover up
     what he did?

2.   Other than money,
     what else do some people
     steal from the places they work?

3.   If you were Che,
     would you have fired Jose?

CHAPTER 10

When Che got home,
he made a list.
He wrote down
all the problems
at his restaurant.
Then he wrote down
different ways
to handle the problems.

One problem
was keeping workers.
Maybe he could
give them
more money.
Maybe that
would make them
want to stay longer.
But where
would he get
the money?

Another problem
was stealing
by a worker.
Che must take
tight control
of every penny.

And too many workers
showed up late.
Che would take pay
from late workers.
Every late minute
would cost them money.

What about fires
in the kitchen?
Everyone must be
more careful.
Che would buy
new fire extinguishers.

The restaurant
had been robbed, too.
Che would keep

less money there
at one time.
Maybe he would
carry a gun, too.

Finally, Chicken by Che
needed to feed
more people.
Che wanted
to put ads
in the paper.
But ads
cost money.
And money
was one thing
Che did not have.

Thinking It Over

1. What are some good ways to get the word around about business?

2. Do you like a job better if you get paid more?

3. Should a worker not get paid for any time missed by coming late?

4. Do you think Che should carry a gun?

CHAPTER 11

The next day
Che went
to the bank.
He asked
for more money.

Mr. Glass
did not want
to give Che
another loan.
"You already
have a hard time
keeping up
every month,"
he said.

"I want
to put ads
in the paper,"
said Che.
"Ads bring

more people.
And more people
bring more money.
I need money
to pay for the ads."

"You have
another problem, Che,"
said Mr. Glass.
"Many people
are afraid
to come
to Chicken by Che.
They are afraid
of fires.
They are afraid
someone will come
and rob the place.
Maybe you should
give up the restaurant.
Don't let things
get any worse."

"Please give me
one more chance,"

said Che.
"I'll get
the people back.
And if the ads
don't work,
I'll pay you back anyway."

"OK, Che,"
said Mr. Glass.
"I believe
in you.
We'll give you
another loan.
But this is
the last one
you'll get
from this bank."

Thinking It Over

1. If you were Mr. Glass,
   would you give Che the loan?

2. Do you think Che
   should give up
   on the restaurant?

3. Do you think people
   should always get
   one more chance?

CHAPTER 12

Norma was not
as happy as Che
about the new loan.
"Chicken by Che
is not even close
to making money,"
she said.
"It's hard enough
to pay the bank now.
And we don't
have enough
to live on at home.
Besides, we're tired
of eating chicken
all the time!"

"I did not think
this would be so hard,"
said Che.
"But I still believe

Chicken by Che
is a good idea.
It's on the right corner.
I just know
we can make it.
I want
to stick
with the restaurant,
no matter what.
We must get over
these troubles,
that's all."

"There will be
more troubles
to come,"
said Norma.

"Maybe,"
said Che.
"But now
I'll be ready
to handle them."

Thinking It Over

1. Do you think that troubles
    can teach you
    how to handle more troubles?

2. What good ideas have you had
    that you believed in
    no matter what?

3. Do you think
    Che should have talked
    to Norma
    before he went to the bank?

CHAPTER 13

A boy named Pedro
came to the restaurant
looking for a job.
He was
very interested
in the restaurant business.
He wanted Che
to teach him
more about it.
And he had some things
to teach Che, too.

"I am
full of ideas,"
said Pedro.
"Here's one idea.
Let's get
other companies
to pay
for our place mats.

We can print
their names
on the place mats.
We'll even make money
on their ads.
And here's another idea.
We can hand out
special tickets
around the neighborhood.
That is where
most of the business
comes from, right?"

"Yes, it is,"
said Che.

"People with special tickets
will pay less
for their food,"
explained Pedro.
"They'll love it!"

"Why are you
so full of ideas?"
asked Che.

"Because I believe
in Chicken by Che,"
said Pedro.
"I grew up here.
We never had
a good fast-food restaurant.
Now there is
Chicken by Che!"

"Why should I
believe in you?"
said Che.

"I'm real,"
said Pedro.
"You talk
to my teachers.
They will tell you
I am a good boy.
I want to learn here.
Someday I want
my own restaurant."

"Do you have
any friends?"
asked Che.

"Yes,"
said Pedro.

"Do any of them
need a job?"
asked Che.
"Maybe they
could work here, too."

Thinking It Over

1. Why is Che not so sure
    about Pedro at first?

2. What do you think
    of Pedro's ideas?

3. Why might it be a good idea
    to let Pedro's friends
    work at the restaurant?
    How might it be a bad idea?

CHAPTER 14

Pedro became
Che's best worker.
He brought his friends
to work at the restaurant, too.
His friends
became good workers, too.
And their other friends
all came to eat
at the restaurant.

Che acted on
Pedro's ideas.
He sold ads
for the place mats.
Ten businesses
signed up right away.

He also handed out
special tickets.
People used
the tickets

to save money
on chicken dinners.

Che used
the new loan
to print special tickets
in the paper.
People came
from all over
to eat Chicken by Che.

Chicken by Che became
the place to go.

Other businesses
were glad
to have their names
on the place mats.
It brought them
new business, too.

There were still
some problems.
It was hard
to keep good workers.

They still didn't want
to work weekends.
And Che
still had to spend
a lot of time
at the restaurant.
He had to make sure
everything went right.

Mr. Glass and the bank
were very happy.
Che paid on his loan
every month.
In two years,
the bank gave Che
more money.
He opened
another Chicken by Che
on the other side
of town.

Che was busy
with the new restaurant.
So Pedro took care
of the first restaurant.

"Someday I want
ten Chicken by Che restaurants,"
said Che to Norma.

"One at a time!"
laughed Norma.

"Or maybe I could open
a nice French restaurant,"
said Che.
"Sometimes I get tired
of eating chicken, too."

But Chicken by Che
was a dream come true.
And the more money
Che made,
the better the chicken tasted.

Thinking It Over

1. How could Che
    get workers to want
    to work weekends?

2. What makes a bank
    give a business
    more money?

3. What is your idea
    of a dream come true?